BAZOOKA

Hand-Held Hollow-Charge Anti-Tank Weapons

CLASSIC WEAPONS SERIES

BAZOOKA

HAND-HELD HOLLOW-CHARGE ANTI-TANK WEAPONS

TERRY J. GANDER

DRAWINGS BY LYN HAYWOOD

PARKGATE
BOOKS

First published in 1998 by
PRC Publishing Ltd,
Kiln House, 210 New Kings Road, London SW6 4NZ

This edition published in 1998 by
Parkgate Books Ltd
Kiln House
210 New Kings Road
London SW6 4NZ
Great Britain

British Library Cataloguing in Publication Data:
A catalogue record for this book is available from the British Library.

ISBN 1 90261 615 4

Printed and bound in China

Acknowledgements
A big thank-you to Lyn Haywood for the excellent drawings and for the help of George Forty, Chris Ellis,
and Peter Chamberlain in researching the photographs.

Contents

PAGE 2: Bazooka in action during the latter stages of the war.

RIGHT: *Panzerschreck* in action.

Introduction

ABOVE: New weapons need new defences and the advent of the tank led inevitably to anti-tank weapons and tactics.

BELOW: One approach was the anti-tank gun, here exemplified by the devastating German 88mm. However, it quickly became obvious that infantry needed something that was smaller, lighter and man-portable.

THE APPEARANCE OF the first British tanks on the Somme battlefields in late 1916 opened a new chapter in the age-old struggle between attack and defence.

When they first appeared the British tanks seemed to be invulnerable, yet it was not long before German front-line troops discovered that reversing 7.92mm rifle bullets in their cartridges before firing them could sometimes allow penetration of the relatively thin steel protection of the tanks—and if it didn't the molten lead splash from the bullet strikes could find a way through joints between armour plates and inconvenience tank crews. Once light field guns had been emplaced close to where tanks might appear, the old tussle between defence and attack was once more under way.

By the time of the Armistice the first specialised anti-tank weapon, the Mauser 13mm *Tankgewehr* anti-tank rifle, had appeared, so to retain their crew protection levels tanks had to acquire more armour. Attack versus defence once more settled down to its time-honoured swing of one

side temporarily overcoming the other until new techniques or equipments tipped the scale in the other direction.

At first it seemed as if the balance was rather fine. The clumsy *Tankgewehr* rifle promised that the foot soldier would be able to retaliate against tanks but armour increases on the part of the tank could easily render small projectiles obsolete. It was a simple matter of kinetic energy. The thicker tank armour grew, the greater the energy needed to punch a way through. The laws of physics dictate that there are practical limits imposed by mass and velocity, the main constituents of anti-tank kinetic energy, just as there are limits to the concentrations of armour a tank can carry, for weight, manoeuvrability and cost also impose their practical limits.

By 1939 the first anti-tank guns were in widespread service. To allow portability and ease of handling by as few personnel as possible these guns were small, with calibres in the 37mm to 40mm bracket, firing high velocity solid steel projectiles well able to penetrate the tank armour of the period. Yet as early as 1940 tanks demonstrated that they had already assumed thicker armoured mantles, proof against such small projectiles. The only immediate recourse was for anti-tank gun calibres to increase to deliver armour-piercing projectiles with greater mass and velocity, and grow they did in leaps and bounds. As one example, between 1940 and 1945 German anti-tank gun calibres leapt from 37mm to 50mm, then to 75mm and 88mm, and finally to 128mm. Even before the calibre of 128mm had been reached the guns involved were heavier than field artillery pieces. They were massive heavy equipments, impossible to move without large gun crews and powerful tractors. The limits

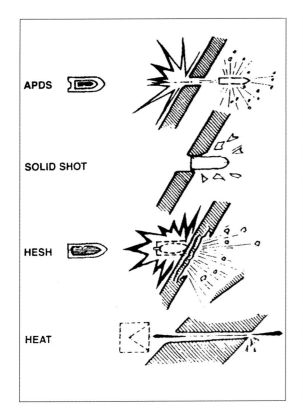

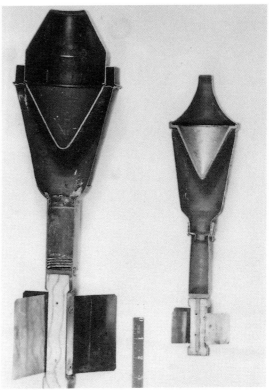

of kinetic energy as an anti-armour weapon were past their practical boundaries.

However, the old attack versus defence balance had already swung in favour of attack with the adoption of the Munroe Effect. The Munroe Effect introduced chemical energy to the anti-tank arena.

The Effect

As long ago as 1887-88 an American chemist, Charles Edward Munroe (1849-1938), first described a phenomenon observed while testing armour plate for the US Navy. When explosive blocks that had a concave cavity in their surface were placed in close proximity to a hard material such as steel or rock, detonating the explosive produced a marked depression in the surface immediately opposite the cavity. This became known as the Munroe Effect. Little heed was taken of it at the time, for it seemed to have no practical applications, although German patents involving the Munroe Effect were taken out as early as 1910 for possible employment in mining.

There the matter rested until the late 1920s when it was further discovered by German researchers Neumann, Neubauer and Thomanek that by carefully shaping the cavity in the explosive and adding a thin metal liner, the results could be spectacular in creating deep penetrations of hardened steel and other materials. This innovation became generally known as the Neumann Effect and was soon fairly common knowledge in the circles dealing with the properties of explosives.

Gradually the outlines of what became known as the hollow or shaped charge became better understood. The general principle is that, as the explosive surrounding a conical cavity (the hollow charge) is detonated, the resultant pressure waves within the cone create sufficient chemical energy to raise localised temperatures to extremely high levels, thereby transforming the cavity's metal liner into a thin molten jet containing metal particles and gases of extremely high energy and temperature. This fluid jet is propelled forward at high velocity (about 9,100m/sec) by the force of the explosion towards the opposite surface, using its energy to gouge a path through whatever is in its way.

Ideally the thin metal liner should be

one of the finer metals such as gold or silver, but economics meant that copper, zinc alloys or steel were substituted. Further refinements introduced trumpet shapes or other outlines to the conical liner to enhance penetration performances. Among other discoveries was that to gain the best results the hollow charge had to be ignited from behind the explosive (using a base igniter) and it had to be detonated at an optimum distance from the surface to be penetrated for best results. This stand-off distance varies with the diameter, length, explosive composition and other properties of the hollow charge involved, but as a very rough guide the distance has to be from two to five cone diameters. The correct stand-off distance enables the high temperature jet to assume its optimum shape and velocity for penetration.

One important attribute of the hollow charge is that its on-target effects are not dependent on range, as they are with kinetic energy projectiles. As they rely on chemical energy, not on mass and velocity, the Munroe and Neumann Effects can work equally well at both extreme and close delivery ranges.

The German military establishment was among the first to exploit the hollow charge by applying liner-enhanced hollow-charge warheads to just about every German artillery and tank gun calibre in service. However, results did not work out quite as expected.

Combat encounters revealed that while hollow charge gun projectile warheads could be effective, the practical penetration results were well below what had been forecast. Further laboratory work and high speed photography provided the first indications of the reasons why as early as 1940.

The main penetration inhibitor was the inherent speed of rotation of gun projectiles. Spin imparted on firing by barrel rifling stabilised the projectile during its trajectory but that same spin created sufficient centrifugal force to disrupt the proper formation of the high temperature jet and significantly reduced its on-target efficiency to as low as one quarter of what could be achieved without the degrading spin. The only solution was somehow to remove or reduce the spin factor, either by adding tail fins or some other form of ballistic drag to the projectile, or by delivering the projectile without spin in the first place.

This account outlines how the defence technicians of three nations went about the task of delivering effective hollow-charge warheads against tank armour. It has to be emphasised that although the German defence establishment was well to the fore in the investigation and exploitation of the hollow charge, it was not alone. Exploitation of the hollow charge was in progress in Switzerland and the United Kingdom at around the same time period as in Germany and the USA. Exactly how is described below.

The importance of the introduction of the portable launcher-delivered hollow-charge projectile to armoured warfare cannot be over-emphasised. For the first time, individual front-line soldiers had at their disposal a means of defeating even the heaviest tanks they were likely to encounter. No longer did the front line infantry have to rely on defensive weapons remote from their control whenever enemy armour appeared in the vicinity.

A further importance must be given to these weapons by considering that those mentioned here were the forerunners of the modern portable anti-armour weapons now commonplace within all the world's armed forces. From the Bazooka and *Panzerschreck* and the associated *Panzerfaust* and PIAT grew a whole host of anti-armour weapons that have once again balanced the old contest between attack and defence. No longer does the tank reign supreme over the battlefield. Tanks can still give the infantry a hard time and remain the foot soldier's worst enemy, that is unless a hollow-charge projection system is to hand. It is no comfort to tank crews that their multi-million dollar chariots are always vulnerable to a single soldier armed with a portable hollow-charge projector.

If all this were not enough, the hollow charge is also highly effective against targets other than tanks. The hollow charge can also be devastatingly effective against field fortifications and structures, including reinforced concrete, once again providing infantrymen with extended firepower capability entirely at their own disposal, enabling them to tackle targets once the province of heavy weapons or the set-piece attack. Hollow charges are equally effective when applied to combat engineer demolition charges.

Rockets

THE ROCKET IS as old as artillery, if not older. For most of its early existence the rocket was regarded as an amusing firework, but by the late Middle Ages rockets were in use as war weapons in India and China, although their military utility seems to have been more directed towards frightening horses than as lethal weapons. The Congreve and Hale artillery rockets were among the first serious war rockets but they displayed all the drawbacks of their type.

Rockets proved to be inaccurate, unreliable and difficult to store and handle. Set against those shortcomings they were also relatively cheap, effective against unprepared enemy troops due to their noise and erratic trajectories, and they were portable enough to be transported to firing locations that more conventional artillery could not even contemplate. Yet by the end of the 19th century the war rocket was in what seemed to be a terminal decline.

The main problem for all early war rocket practitioners involved the propellants they had to utilise, all of them black powder based. It was only with the advent of double-based propellants in the early years of the 20th century that any practical alternative arose. Double-based propellants could be extruded through dies to form large one-piece 'grains' that could be arranged to burn evenly and reasonably consistently, thereby doing away with many of the disadvantages of the older rocket propellants, although even today complete burn consistency, and therefore rocket trajectory accuracy, can never be completely achieved. The German Krupp concern was in the forefront of the corresponding early artillery rocket development in Germany but little came of its research investments prior to 1918.

The Germans were not alone in investigating the possibilities of double-based rocket propellants. The American Robert H. Goddard (1882-1945), now acknowledged as one of the fathers of modern rocketry, was an early exponent of the modern war rocket. As early as 1918 he was demonstrating a shoulder-launched rocket system that could be carried and operated by an individual. One of the first rockets Goddard demonstrated weighed 3.5kg (7.7lb) and carried a high explosive warhead to a range of 1,200m (4,000ft). This was only one of a series of similar rockets produced by Goddard, the largest of which weighed 20kg (44lb). Illustrations of these early rocket systems are few but they indicate that their shoulder launchers were simple tubes not too unlike the developments of 20 years later.

The end of the war in 1918 ended Goddard's early military rocket experiments, leaving him to proceed to liquid propulsion rocket motors and similar matters. There were few within the US military hierarchy who regarded Goddard's experiments with any enthusiasm, for the concept had been overtaken in tactical terms by payload delivery systems such as the Stokes Mortar, which delivered greater ranges with accuracy, utilised conventional propellants and did not involve the operator having to stand in the open to launch the projectile. Some US-funded investigations into rockets did commence during the 1930s but the aftermath of the Depression and a general lack of defence spending and resources led to no conclusive results.

The Soviet Union was another early investigator of war rockets. In 1931 B. S. Petropawlovski developed the 65mm calibre RS65, a tube pattern, shoulder-launched system not unlike later developments elsewhere, complete with a shield

for the firer. The project appears to have been inconclusively terminated, doubtless as a side result of Stalin's military purges of the late 1930s. The Soviet Union never did develop further anti-armour weapons similar to those described below prior to 1945, even though they became the greatest user of artillery rockets of World War 2.

Swiss interlude

At this point we have to return to the hollow charge. By the 1930s several nations were investigating the possibilities of the principle, including Germany. However, much of the attention from the United Kingdom and USA was centred on the Mohaupt Company of Switzerland, from where Henri Mohaupt was issuing glowing descriptions of a new armour-penetrating explosive he claimed to have developed.

An American military observer from the Ordnance Department, Captain Studler, was assigned to Bern where he formed a link with a British commission which was also attempting to discover more about Mohaupt's claims. The British group observed a practical demonstration of the explosive in question and shared the test results with Captain Studler. They, like him, soon came to the conclusion that Neumann-inspired extensions of the old Munroe Effect were involved and British interest waned, especially when the Mohaupt company demanded a substantial fee for any further disclosure of their development. Having witnessed what Mohaupt could do, the British went home and initiated their own hollow charge experiments along similar lines.

Mohaupt also met an unresponsive reaction from the US Ordnance Dept, especially as he requested $25,000 in advance payments before further negotiations could progress. That was in mid-1940. Considering the lack of British interest and that the US Treasury deemed such sums out of the question, it seemed the Mohaupt episode was concluded.

It was not. In late 1940 Henri Mohaupt

turned up in Washington with an example of an anti-armour rifle grenade employing his 'secret' principle. 200 trial examples were successfully tested at the Aberdeen Proving Ground in Maryland, with the ensuing recommendation that the Mohaupt design be adopted. At this point it emerged that a similar design from an American source had already been proposed and rejected by the Ordnance Department.

By early 1940 Nevil Monroe Hopkins had already suggested an anti-armour bomb with a hollow charge warhead, only to be told that his idea was not new as it

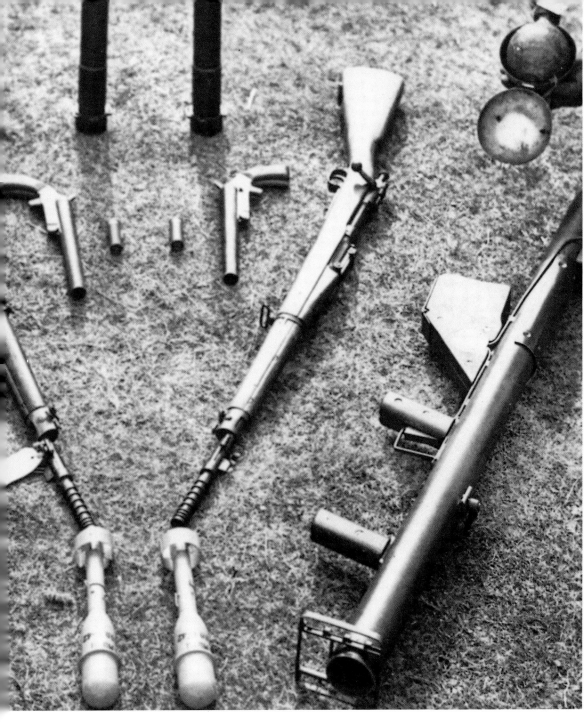

LEFT: An assortment of anti-tank weapons with M1 Bazookas either side, two M1903 Springfield rifles with muzzle attachments for the M9A1 anti-tank grenades nearby plus flare pistols and projectors. The object at top right of the photograph is a 'Sticky Bomb'.

was based on German patents dating back to 1911 (which were based on the unpatented Munroe findings.) Thus Mohaupt's 'secret' was no secret after all and was already known to the US Ordnance Dept. The outcome of this left hand/right hand activity within the department was that the Mohaupt grenade was purchased but the Swiss entrepreneur had to be content with a lesser fee!

Two Mohaupt pattern grenades were type-classified: the M9A1 to be launched from muzzle attachments on 0.30in rifles and the M10 to be projected from 0.50in M2 Browning heavy machine guns. In both cases launch propulsion was provided by blank cartridges; however, the stresses imparted to the launch weapon on firing were significant and could inflict degrading damage following prolonged use.

In the event the M9A1 rifle grenade was issued and employed in combat. It weighed 0.59kg (1.3lb) and could penetrate up to about 105mm (4in) of armour under ideal conditions. The M10 for the M2 machine gun did not fare so well and was not issued on any scale, if at all. Instead it was to follow another service career.

Bazooka

ABOVE: An early example of a 2.36in M1 Bazooka on a training range, circa 1942.

ABOVE RIGHT: An illustration taken from a German recognition manual showing an M1 launcher and an M6 rocket; the German designation was RPzB 788(a).

FAR RIGHT: A 2.36in M6 rocket showing the original tail fins.

IN 1933 THE US Army assigned a single officer, Captain Skinner, to investigate the possibilities of rockets as weapons. As mentioned above, research funds were at a premium during the 1930s so Captain Skinner's activities were somewhat restricted until 1940 when the M9/M10 rifles grenades were procured. As it was appreciated that the launch stresses imparted by launching such grenades were substantial, it was decided to investigate the use of rockets to deliver similar warheads.

The US Navy was also investigating the potential of rockets at the US Navy Ground at Indian Head, Maryland. For once the old Army/Navy rivalry was overlooked in favour of a common objective. Captain Skinner and a Lieutenant Uhl of the US Navy arranged to work together, with Captain Skinner adding a rocket motor to an M10 grenade warhead while Lieutenant

Uhl, soon to be a Captain, worked out the basics for a steel tube pattern launcher with the necessary firing controls and mechanisms. Working in cooperation with a team of civilian scientists led by Doctor Hickman of the National Research Defence Committee (NRDC), by May 1942 the first test rigs were ready for firing demonstrations.

The appearance of the rudimentary tube launcher during the Aberdeen Proving Ground demonstrations gave rise to a quip that it resembled the comedian Bob Burns' Bazooka, the name given to one of his props—an oversize cigar. The name stuck and from then on the launcher was the Bazooka, a name that endures to this day and is generally applied to just about every similar tube pattern rocket launcher ever produced.

Although the Aberdeen Proving Ground demonstrations featured 2.36in (60mm) dummy warheads being fired against moving tank targets, the results were impressive enough for immediate orders to be placed by the US Army. An initial verbal order for 5,000 launchers and 25,000 rockets (plus 5,000 practice rockets) was soon expanded, using more formal procedures, to 75,000 launchers and an initial 120,000 rockets. Having gained valuable practical experience from the project, the US Navy withdrew from future involvement to concentrate on more suitable-to-service rocket projects.

On 30 June 1942 the US Army Ordnance Committee type-classified the 2.36in (6cm) launcher as the Launcher, Rocket, A.T., 2.36in, M1; the associated rocket became the Rocket High Explosive Anti-Tank (HEAT), 2.36in M6. Inert practice rockets became the M7. This rocket and launcher combination heralded the first

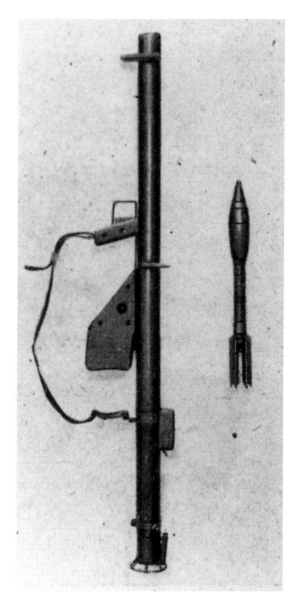

use of rockets in combat by the US Army since the Civil War.

Production began almost immediately for there were no great technological or manufacturing challenges to be overcome. The E. G. Budd company started to manufacture the rockets with the double-base propellant, known as Ballistite, provided by the Hercules Powder Company; later propellant producers included the DuPont, Atlas Powder and American Cyanamid companies. General Electric at Bridgeport was asked to produce 5,000 M1 launchers within 30 days (it did so with 89 minutes to spare) and then go on to manufacture a further 60,000 by the end of 1942. The 1943 target was put at 100,000 launchers and by 1945 General Electric had produced some

450,000 launchers, assisted by more than 100 subcontractors.

As it turned out, the rush to production almost inevitably brought problems in its train. By May 1943 cases had been reported of rocket motors detonating within the launcher tube so not only was the rear tube exterior reinforced with wire coils but a revised motor containing less Ballistite propellant was introduced (without degrading overall performance), while a different grade of steel tubing was used to contain the rocket motor. In addition, the rocket igniter was replaced by a more reliable component. These changes, introduced in the field by travelling teams of technicians who ventured as far as combat areas, resulted in another new designation for the rockets of HEAT M6A1; practice rockets became the M7A1. Modified launchers became the M1A1.

A further round of rocket modifications, this time introduced on the production lines, involved a change of outline for the streamlined ballistic cover, or "ogive", to a domed contour over the front of the rocket warheads to improve the angle of incidence against target armour (the original more pointed ogive could cause the rocket to slide off target armour at low graze angles), while the original tail fins were replaced by a more effective drum stabiliser assembly. A more important internal modification involved the original Mohaupt warhead hollow charge steel liner being replaced by a thin copper liner to improve penetration performance. Other changes to what became the HEAT M6A3 rocket (there was no known service issue of the interim M6A2) included improved waterproofing for the base detonating fuze. Practice rockets became the M7A3. A later and improved impact fuze, the M400A1, gave rise to yet another new rocket designation, the HEAT M6A5.

Rockets were transported and issued packed into cardboard tubes intended to be carried by launcher crews in an awkward-looking bandolier garment slung over

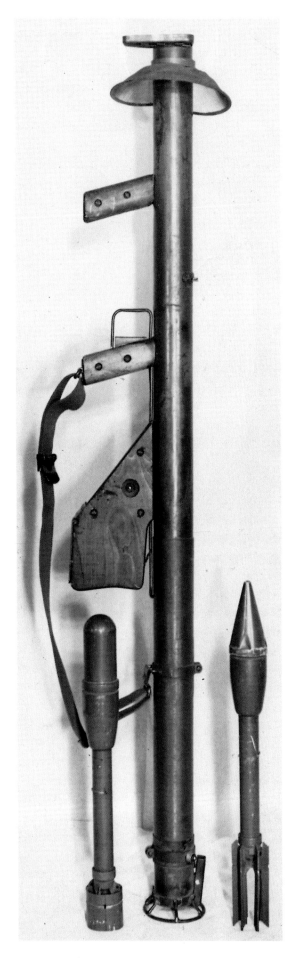

RIGHT: 2.36in M1 Bazooka in an as-issued condition complete with wire mesh ring close to the muzzle. The right-hand rocket is an M6A1 with an M6A5 rocket on the left.

the chest and back so that three tubes could be carried on the chest and another three on the back. It is interesting to note that few illustrations of Bazooka crews in action depict these garments so it must be assumed that they were not used to any great extent.

An M10 rocket with a smoke warhead filled with white phosphorous was type-classified; development work on associated incendiary and chemical warheads was never completed. A proposed high velocity (500ft (152m)/sec) 2.36in rocket known as the T59 carrying a powerful 3.63kg (7.9in) HEAT warhead never overcame considerable technical difficulties so the project was eventually terminated, despite considerable development efforts to iron out the bugs over a six-year period.

Another odd development item was an attempt to produce a 2.36in (6cm) rocket with an anti-personnel blast/fragmentation warhead. This consisted of two Mark 2A1 'pineapple' hand grenades attached in tandem to a standard rocket motor and fin assembly. The grenades were mounted complete with safety pins and safety fly off levers so exactly how the device was supposed to work remains something of a mystery. The only thing that is certain regarding this odd item is that it was never used in action. It now seems fairly certain that this blast/fragmentation rocket was an improvisation dreamed up by someone who had never been in combat!

Popular and effective though the 2.36in M1/M1A1 launchers were, they were 1.37m (4.5ft) long overall and were thus somewhat awkward to carry, even though a webbing sling was provided. Airborne troops and jungle combatants in particular found the overall length too unwieldy for their tactical requirements. As the M1/M1A1 launcher was no more than a length of steel pipe it did not take long for someone to devise a method of dividing the tube—via central bayonet coupling rings—into two parts for transport, resulting in the slightly longer M9 launcher; the

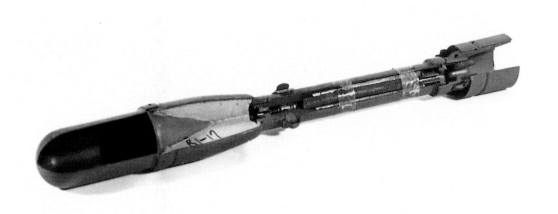

LEFT: Cross-section of a 2.36in M6A5 rocket showing the hollow charge and the outline of the revised ogive.

BELOW LEFT: On the training ranges with a 2.36in M1 launcher in the process of being loaded; note the ammunition bandolier garments; these are rarely seen in combat photographs.

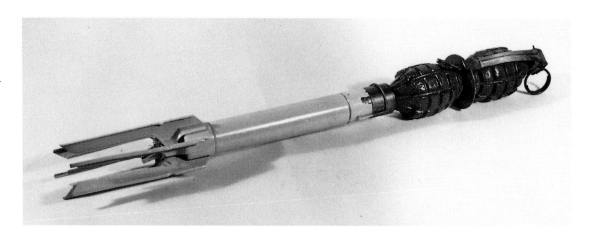

RIGHT: A 1944 photograph of the proposed 2.26in rocket with a high explosive/fragmentation warhead made up from two Mark 2A1 hand grenades. This proposal was not accepted for service

BELOW: Loading a 2.36in M9 launcher on a training range.

Bazooka Model	M1/M1A1	M9/M9A1
Calibre of tube	60mm (2.34in)	60mm
Length of tube	1.37m	1.55m
Weight of launcher	5.9kg	5.96kg
Weight of rocket	1.54kg	1.54kg
Velocity	83m/sec	83m/sec
Max range	640m	640m
Penetration	120mm	120mm

LEFT: A drawing of the 2.36in M9A1 launcher; the M9 was visually identical. *L. Haywood*

FAR LEFT: Comparison of a 2.36-inch M1A1 launcher on the left with a two-piece M9A1 launcher on the right.

M9A1 involved only a few minor manufacturing changes to the coupling. All the main weapon 'services', such as the shoulder stock, firing and loading arrangements and trigger assembly, were located on the rear portion of the divided tube. At the same time the opportunity was taken to replace the original battery-powered rocket ignition system by a more reliable magneto driven system manufactured by Magnavox (see below).

Some production of the M9/M9A1 launcher was shared by the Cheney Bigelow Wire Works of Springfield who also devised and produced a lightened aluminium version of the M9A1 known as the M18. The M18 was supposed to be issued to airborne troops but only about 500 had been manufactured by the time the war ended and none reached combat.

Wartime production of 2.36in launchers reached a grand total of 475,628, along with 15,603,000 rockets.

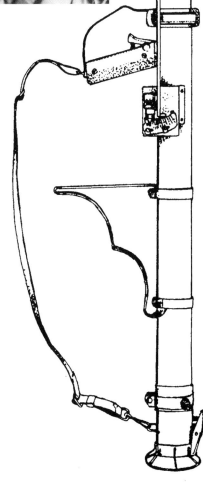

Rakentenwerfer and *Panzerschreck*

COMPARED TO THE interwar American rocket research programme, that carried out by the Germans was almost intensive. As early as 1931 a rocket research establishment had been set up by the German Army at the Kummersdorf West weapon testing ranges, to the south of Berlin, while the Luftwaffe had its own equivalent organisation at Tarnewitz. The German Army research programme initially led to a number of small calibre solid fuel rockets, including a 73mm (2.9in) diameter series intended for the dissemination of propaganda leaflets over front lines. Another project involved a 65mm (2.5in) air defence rocket intended to be launched in salvos. Longer term research and development led to the larger calibre *Nebelwerfer* multiple launch artillery rocket systems that entered Germany Army service from 1940 onwards.

Thus when a requirement for a German anti-tank rocket carrying a hollow charge was issued, the rocket technology was already to hand. The first German anti-tank rocket, the *Raketenpanzerbüchse Granate* (RPzBGr) 4312, was approved for service during late 1942, the first examples appearing from the production lines in 1943.

The RPzBGr 4312 had a warhead diameter of 88mm (3.4in). As with other warheads of its type, the hollow charge was protected in flight by a streamlined ballistic cover which had on its extended tip an impact sensor connected to a base fuze behind the hollow charge explosive, a 60/40 mix of RDX/TNT with a mild steel liner 0.15mm (6/100,000in) thick. The combination of extended tip and cover provided the required stand-off distance to enable the warhead to penetrate a very respectable 160mm (6.24in) of armour plate set at an angle of 60°. In-flight stabilisation was provided by drum fins at the end of the tubular steel tail boom containing the solid propellant rocket motor. The

RIGHT: An 8.8cm RPzB 43 compared with the British 0.55in Boys anti-tank rifle.

Raketenwerfer 43 Puppchen	
Calibre	88m (3.5in)
Length of barrel	1.6m (5ft 3in)
Weight in action	100kg (220lb)
Muzzle velocity	150m/sec
	(492ft/sec)
Range (anti-tank)	230m (750ft)
Rocket weight	2.66kg (5.85lb)

latter contained seven sticks of a double-base propellant held in place by wire grids.

To deliver this rocket German designers appear to have at first over-reached themselves, for their first launcher offering was the 8.8cm (3.5in) *Raketenwerfer 43 Puppchen* (Rocket thrower 43 Dolly), manufactured by the Westfallische-Anhaltische-Sprengstoff AG at Reinsdorf. Intended for issue to the anti-tank companies of infantry divisions, the R-Werfer 43 resembled a lightly-constructed miniature artillery piece complete with a shield, although the latter was intended as much to protect the firer from the rocket exhaust as against incoming fire. It appears that as the launcher was intended to be deployed by German Army anti-tank companies, it was thought the launcher might as well resemble a conventional anti-tank gun.

Weight in action was 100kg (220lb) so to move the weapon it had to be towed on removable wheels; it could also be broken down into seven loads for pack transport. In action the R-Werfer 43 rested on two rockers and a trail spade. There were no fire controls as all aiming was carried out by moving the R-Werfer 43 on the rockers.

Aiming provisions were very basic and consisted of simple fixed iron sights. The slight recoil was absorbed by the carriage as there was no other recoil attenuation system.

The rocket was loaded into a breech with a sliding block and fired using a percussion cap to ignite the rocket motor. The maximum range of the R-Werfer 43 was stated to be 700m (2,300ft), although 500m (1,640ft) was more likely. Its maximum effective range against moving tank targets was limited to 230m (750ft). Rocket weight on loading was 2.66kg (5.85lb).

While the 8.8cm rocket held considerable promise, the R-Werfer 43 was not exactly what the infantry were looking for. However, almost as soon as the R-Werfer 43 entered production it was rendered obsolete by the fortunes of war. In late 1942, when the US Army joined the Operation 'Torch' campaign to clear the Germans and Italians from North Africa, they took with them the first combat examples of the M1 Bazooka, and its associated M6 HEAT rockets. Inevitably, examples of the M1 Bazooka fell into German hands and were whisked away to Germany for examination and evaluation at the Wehrmacht Weapons Testing Ground at Kummersdorf. For their administrative and recognition purposes the Germans designated the American Bazooka as the 6cm RPzB 788(a), although for some unfathomable reason early German reports on the Bazooka referred to it as the Stanley anti-tank rifle.

The unexpected advent of the M1 Bazooka in Tunisia made a considerable impact on the German military establishment. Not only did the Bazooka concept present a considerable danger to German armour but the simplicity, low cost and potential of the launcher's design made a great impression.

The immediate result was the abandonment of the R-Werfer 43 in favour of the novel Bazooka rocket delivery system. Within weeks the first examples of the 8.8cm (3.4in) *Raketenpanzerbüchse* 43 (8.8cm RPzB 43) were coming off the HASAG production line at Meuselwitz. Most R-Werfer 43s already produced were sent to Tunisia or Italy and were soon forgotten or lost in action. A few were diverted to be emplaced among the defensive works covering the Normandy beaches as part of the Atlantic Wall defences.

The RPzB 43 *Panzerschreck* (Tank Terror) was an enlarged version of the M1

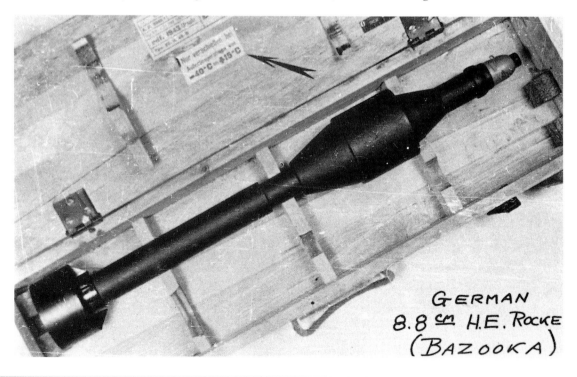

RIGHT: An 8.8cm RPzB 4322 rocket in its transport crate.

GERMAN 8.8 cm H.E. ROCKE (BAZOOKA)

LEFT: An 8.8cm RPzB 54 launcher complete with a RPzBGr 4322 rocket.

Bazooka, being scarcely more than a length of steel tube with a shoulder rest and firing arrangements attached, hence the alternative German nickname of *Ofenrohr* (Stovepipe). The calibre was selected simply because 8.8cm (3.4in) hollow charge warheads were already in production for launching from the R-Werfer 43, but with rockets for the RPzB 43 there was a difference. Having noted that the American M6 HEAT rocket was ignited electrically, the German rocket ignition method was altered accordingly, resulting in the RPzBGr 4322, weighing 3.25kg (7.2lb). However, the Germans decided not to adopt the battery-powered ignition circuitry, rapidly developing and adopting a magneto-driven ignition method, of which more below. It is interesting to note that the Americans later adopted a magneto ignition system for their M9/M9A1 launchers.

The weight of a loaded 8.8cm RPzB 43 was 9.5kg (20.9lb). Armour penetration performance remained as before, ie 160mm (6.24in) of armour plate set at an angle of 60°.

The length of the RPzB 43 (1.64m/5ft 5in) meant that to handle it effectively called for a team of two, one acting as loader and carrying five ready-use rockets on a special backpack frame. Only when a target approached was a rocket loaded into the rear of the launching tube, where it was held by a retaining catch, and connected (by the loader) to the firing circuit via two thin wires. The firer used simple fixed sights for aiming and cocked the firing arrangements by pulling back a spring-loaded lever. Operating the trigger produced a current for a primer to ignite the rocket motor and launch the rocket.

RPzB 43 teams had to be masters of concealment and stealth for the practical range of the RPzBGr 4322 rocket was a maximum of 150m (492ft). Combat ranges were frequently considerably less. A trained team could launch four or five rockets in one minute, not only against tanks: *Panzerschreck* warheads were also highly effective against field fortifications or buildings during fighting in built up areas.

The RPzB 43 was very rapidly accepted into service and soon became the preferred portable anti-tank weapon for infantry formations. By 1944 the weapon was so well integrated that each infantry regiment had an establishment of 36 held by the regimental anti-tank company, along with three 7.5cm (2.9in) Pak 40 towed anti-tank guns. The so-called Volksgrenadier infantry regiments of the latter war years were meant to have a planned 72 *Panzerschrecken*.

RIGHT: A typical drill book illustration showing a RPzB 54 being loaded.

BELOW: US Army troops fooling with a captured 8.8cm RPzB 54 launcher.

Panzerschreck			
Model	RPzB 43	RPzB 54	RpzB 54/1
Calibre	88mm (3.4in)	88mm (3.4in)	88mm (3.4in)
Length of barrel	1.64m (5ft 5in)	1.64m (5ft 5in)	1.35m (5ft 0.25in)
Weight	9.5kg (20.9lb)	11kg (24.2lb)	9.5kg (20.9lb)
Muzzle velocity	110m/sec (361ft/sec)	110m/sec (361ft/sec)	110m/sec (361ft/sec)
Range (anti-tank)	150m (c500ft)	150m (c500ft)	180m (c500ft)
Rocket weight	3.25kg (7.2lb)	3.25kg (7.2lb)	3.25kg (7.2lb)

BELOW: A comparison between the M1A1 Bazooka (centre) and the German 8.8cm RPzB 43 (top); the third weapon is a 3.5in M20 Super Bazooka (bottom).

By mid-1944 the RPzB 43 was well into the process of being withdrawn from front line units in favour of the improved 8.8cm (3.4in) RPzB 54; the RPzB 43s were transferred to second line and home defence militias. The main change on the RPzB 54 was the introduction of a shield for the firer; the weight increased to 11kg (24.2lb).

By 1944 the *Panzerschreck* series had already become so important that production was in progress at seven centres and many others were concerned with sub-assemblies. The simplicity of the RPzB 54 and its lack of demand for critical raw materials or manufacturing resources was such that the unit cost was only RM70. Production totals during 1943 and 1944 reached 289,151.

By the end of 1944 production was already switching to the 8.8cm (3.4in) RPzB 54/1 capable of launching an improved rocket, the RPzBGr 4992. While the armour penetrating warhead remained as before, the RPzBGr 4992 was modified by having a far more efficient motor which completely consumed its propellant by the time it left the muzzle. The exhaust hazard to the firer therefore no longer existed, except under extremely low temperature conditions, although the safety area to the rear still had to be observed.

The improved RPzBGr 4992 motor also increased the maximum range to 180m (c600ft) while at the same time allowing the overall length of the launch tube to be reduced from the former 1.64m (5ft 5in) to a handier 1.35m (5ft 0.25in); the weight reverted to 9.5kg (20.9lb). RPzB 54/1 production had reached 25,744 by the time the war ended. By then 2,218,400 8.8cm

RPzBGr 4322 and 4992 rockets had also been manufactured.

Bazooka and *Panzerschreck* Compared
Both the Bazooka and *Panzerschreck* were essentially simple rocket launcher systems in design terms, being little more than open-ended smooth-bored steel tubes with firing circuits, sights and shoulder stocks attached. Sights were very simple as all field employment was usually limited to ranges below 150m (c500ft) by the limitations of the rocket motors involved, while the relatively low velocities of the rockets meant they were susceptible to environmental influences, such as side winds, that could alter the trajectory considerably. To be sure of hitting a tank-sized target the launcher crews therefore had to be situated uncomfortably close to their quarry.

The original M1/M1A1 Bazooka utilised an electrical ignition circuit to ignite a small squib in the rocket motor tail; the small electrical current involved was provided by two dry cell batteries. Firing

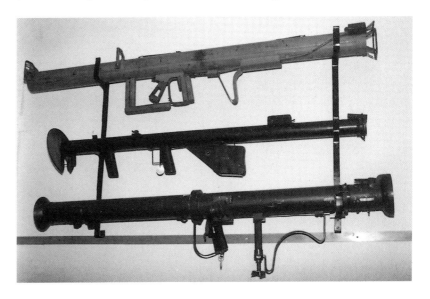

THIS PAGE: Early training-ground views of the M1: note wire guard at front of launcher (RIGHT). This was added to early production M1/M1A1 Bazookas to protect the launcher from the rocket exhausts, which could be harmful to the firer especially under cold weather conditions.

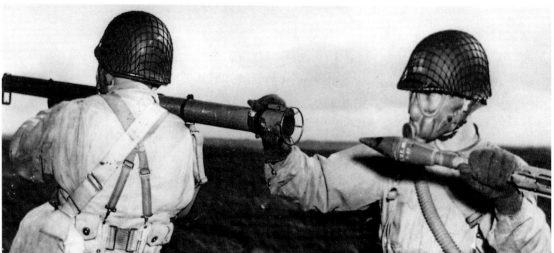

ABOVE: Another early view of the M1—the original caption of this US Army photograph reads: **'US Army's latest weapon.**
The first picture of the new two-man anti-tank rifle . . . which has already been used in the Tunisian campaign'[1942].

LEFT: Two years later, in 1944, a unit of US Seventh Army is seen in the Vosges: note bazooka carrier.

drills dictated that the battery state was checked prior to loading a rocket by observing a circuit tester that illuminated a small light bulb if all was well.

Experience in the field demonstrated that this ignition method could be unsatisfactory. The batteries either became too flat for use when needed most or contact corrosion caused malfunctions, while the supply of fresh batteries meant another item to be provided via already well loaded supply chains. In addition, batteries had to be kept warm under cold conditions so that meant swapping those in the weapon for a spare set carried in a warm place close to the body every 30 minutes or so. The battery compartment in the shoulder stock normally contained four batteries, two in use and two spares.

To overcome these battery-induced disadvantages, when the M9/M9A1 entered service a new magneto-operated ignition system was introduced. For this system, pressing the trigger drove a small magnet through a wire coil to generate the necessary ignition current. On the *Panzerschreck*, from where the M9/M9A1 magneto system

was adopted, the magnet was spring-loaded, the spring being tensioned by cocking a lever located forward of the trigger group prior to operating the trigger. Pulling the trigger released the spring to drive the magnet through the coil.

Rockets interfaced with the firing circuit by two thin wires leading from the rocket motor tail and connected to the launcher circuit by the loader after the rocket had been inserted through the rear of the launcher. Once the rocket was in place it was held by a retaining catch. As soon as the rocket was loaded and connected the loader signalled the firer by tapping his helmet, and then took cover to one side. For the RPzB 54/1 and the improved RPzBGr 4992 rocket, the revised connections to the launcher's electrical circuit did not involve wires as the interface between the launcher and rocket motor was accomplished via two side-located, spring-loaded plungers. With typical German thoroughness, wire connection provisions were retained on the RPzB 54/1 to enable the earlier RPzBGr 4322 rocket to be utilised when necessary.

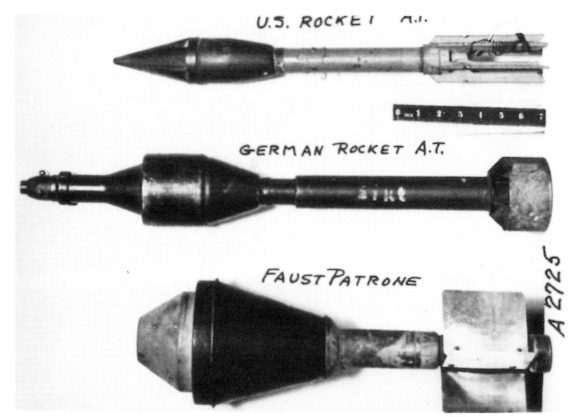

RIGHT: A useful US Army comparison photograph of a 2.36in M6 rocket (top), a 8.8cm RPzBGr 4312 for the R-Werfer 43 (centre) and a Panzerfaust 30 bomb (bottom), wrongly labelled as a *Faustpatrone* bomb.

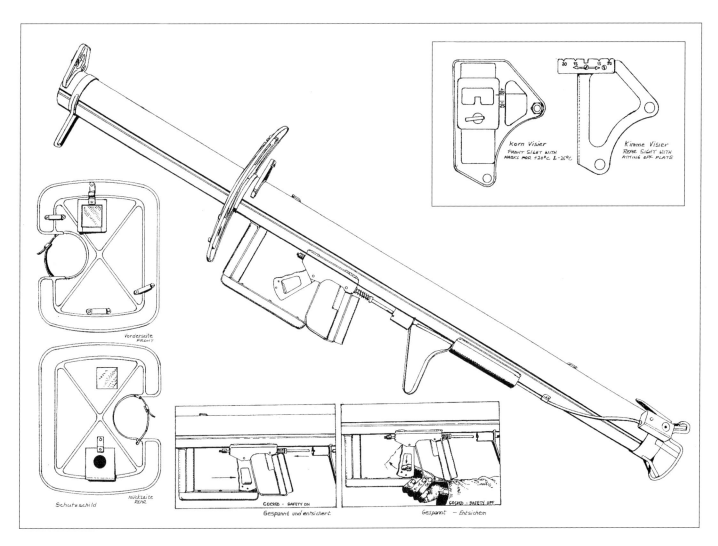

Korn Visier
FRONT SIGHT WITH
MARKS FOR +20°C L-15°C

Kimme Visier
REAR SIGHT WITH
AIMING OFF PLATE

Vorderseite
FRONT

Schutzschild

Rückseite
REAR

COCKED - SAFETY ON
Gespannt und entsichert

COCKED - SAFETY OFF
Gespannt - Entsichern

ABOVE: Detail drawing of an 8.8cm RP 54 launcher depicting its sights. *L. Haywood*

LEFT: Combat photograph of heavily camouflaged *Panzershreck* operator.

29

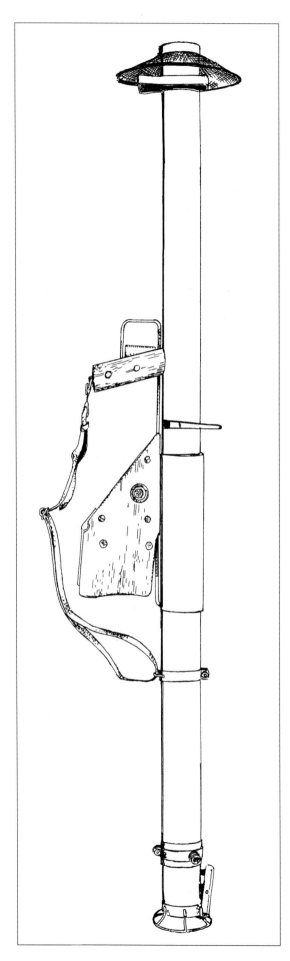

Sighting arrangements for all types of launcher were simple. The sight for the original American Bazooka demonstration launchers in 1941 involved nothing more than a nail picked up from the ground at the firing point. Production M1/M1A1 Bazooka sights were only slightly more sophisticated but by the time the M9/M9A1 was in service some provisions for range and target speed corrections were available; there was even an extended rail bar sight for long-range firing.

Panzerschreck sights were also simple fixed metal pressings but by late 1944, when the RPzB 54/1 first appeared, the conditions under which the launchers had to be deployed imposed some improvements. One was that in the extreme cold winter temperatures or the heat of the summer months experienced on the Eastern Front, the rocket motors burned at differing rates to the extent that trajectory arcs could vary considerably; solid fuel rocket motors, like all explosives, tend to burn more slowly at low temperatures. This could be compensated for by clamping the foresight in one of three possible positions (the foresight of the RPzB 54 had two positions) according to the time of year. The RPzB 54/1 rear sight also had extra notch positions as aids for aiming-off when dealing with varying target crossing speeds.

The early shoulder rest for the M1/M1A1 Bazooka resembled a wooden rifle butt stock. On the later M9/M9A1 these were abandoned in favour of easier to manufacture (and lighter) steel strip shoulder frames so shaped that they could either locate on the shoulder or be rested on the ground (when possible) to steady the aim when firing at longer ranges. The *Panzerschreck* series utilised metal frame shoulder stocks from the outset. Recoil forces when firing both types of weapon were negligible but the flash and exhaust characteristics of the launched rocket could induce flinching with inexperienced firers.

On early production M1/M1A1

ABOVE: A drill book publicity illustration of an early 2.36in M1 launcher being loaded; note the wire mesh shield around the muzzle and that both crew members are wearing goggles and steel helmets.

Bazookas the rocket exhausts could be harmful to the firer as they left the muzzle, especially under cold weather conditions, but it was found that risks could be considerably reduced by mounting a ring of thin wire mesh around the muzzle. As an extra precaution the firer was encouraged to wear goggles. In action both measures were frequently ignored, the flimsy wire mesh soon becoming damaged by handling and snagging to the point of uselessness and subsequent disposal. M9/M9A1 production examples featured a raised flange deflector around the muzzle which largely eradicated all risks to the firer so both the mesh ring and the wearing of goggles became unnecessary. However, according to the drill book, the wearing of a steel helmet remained necessary for both the firer and loader of M1/M1A1 and M9/M9A1 launchers.

With the early *Panzerschreck* rockets, the nature of the slow burning propellant produced a more pronounced firing hazard. As it left the launcher muzzle the rocket motor continued to burn for a distance of about 2m (6ft 6in) so the firer had to be protected against the dangerous exhaust flame and burning propellant particles by wearing a service respirator, steel helmet and chemical protection poncho. With the introduction of the shield on the RPzB 54

and 54/1 the cumbersome protective clothing necessary when firing the RPzB 43 was no longer necessary, although steel helmets were usually retained.

As with the Bazooka, a cone-shaped area behind the RPzB 43 (and its later variants) constituted a danger area for personnel when a rocket was launched, for on ignition an exhaust flame some 4m (13ft) long resulted. Launcher crews and any personnel in the vicinity soon learned of the dangers of the cone shaped exhaust hazard area which, for safety, extended well beyond 4m (13ft). The exhaust hazard also meant that launchers could not be utilised from within enclosed areas or structures.

As mentioned above, most models of *Panzerschreck* and Bazooka were transported by simply carrying them slung on a thin webbing strap from a shoulder, although within some of the better-equipped German units *Panzerschrecken* were carried on horse-drawn carts. One horse pulled a two-wheeled cart containing six launchers on racks, while a second cart connected behind the first carried 30 rockets.

The maximum *Panzerschreck* rocket velocity was 100-110m/sec (328-361ft/sec), faster than that for the Bazooka which was originally 83m/sec (272ft/sec). Postwar Allied intelligence reports laid great emphasis on German rockets being much more reliable and better made than their Bazooka-launched equivalents.

Tank crews came to respect the *Panzerschreck* and Bazooka series but soon came to appreciate that their rockets were not all round wonder weapons. It was discovered that if the rocket warheads could be detonated at a distance of anything over 500mm (20in) from vulnerable tank armour, and not against it, the high temperature armour-piercing jet would lose most of its penetration energy by the time it reached the armour.

At first, this stand-off detonation was rather inefficiently accomplished by field fixes such as draping sandbags and lengths

LEFT: On the road to Paris—US infantry follow an M10 tank destroyer; note mesh on Bazooka muzzle.

BELOW: The M20 3.5in (89mm) 'Super Bazooka' was ready for use by US Marines in Korea.

of spare tank track around the front and sides of tank hulls. More sophisticated measures involved hanging steel wire mesh or thin sheet metal screens on stand-off brackets along the sides of a tank; the Germans called such measures *Schützen* (Skirts). The side screens also had the added bonus that they also helped to keep dust away from tank vision devices. The mesh or metal screens were quite sufficient to cause a rocket warhead impact sensor to function so by the time the high temperature jet reached a tank's main hull armour most of its penetrating potential had been dissipated relatively harmlessly.

The Next Step

As the war ended, American development work was in progress on a M20 3.5in (89mm) 'Super Bazooka' version of the M9/M9A1 launcher and an associated HEAT rocket, the M28. The end of the war ended any further priority development of this model, only for the matter to be restarted under conditions of extreme urgency during the Korean War. Under ideal conditions the M28 rocket warhead could penetrate up to 265mm (10.35in) of armour, with a maximum combat range of 110m (c360ft) against armoured vehicles; rocket weight was 4.04kg (8.9lb).

It is interesting to note that the 'next

step' calibre choice for the US Army was to a warhead size virtually identical to the German wartime counterpart, the 8.8cm *Panzerschreck* series. By contrast, in Germany a 105mm (4.1in) version of the *Panzerschreck* entered development from August 1944 onward. The launcher would have been 2.4m (7ft 10.5in) long launching a rocket weighing 6.1kg (13.4lb) to a range of 300m (984ft). It was intended that the rocket warhead would penetrate up to at least 220mm (6.6in) of armour but the entire project was terminated by the end of the war.

FAR LEFT: Stand-off detonation was one answer to the threat of hollow-charge weapons. Here the inefficient way of trying to achieve this—lengths of spare track around the front and sides of the tank hull.

LEFT AND BELOW: More sophisticated measures—the German *Schützen*, side plates of additional armour.

Panzerfaust

ABOVE: The T-34—its low silhouette, angled armour and sheer production numbers forced the Germans to develop mass-produced, throwaway light anti-tank weapons such as the *Panzerfaust*.

BELOW: Outline drawing of one of the *Faustpatrone* prototypes. *L. Haywood*

AS EARLY AS 1942 the Soviet tanks that continued to appear in seemingly ever-growing numbers on the Eastern Front, in particular the T-34, began to give cause for concern among German military planners and front-line soldiers alike. Due to the generally open nature of the Eastern Front combat zones, Soviet tanks were likely to appear from just about any point of the compass when least expected, so it was well nigh impossible to position or maintain anti-tank defences everywhere they

might be needed. Despite the arrival on the scene of light and portable weapons such as the *Panzerschreck* series, it was gradually appreciated that just about every combat soldier would have to carry some means of defeating tanks in order to keep the Red tank hordes at bay—so the crew-served *Panzerschreck* was not the complete answer.

The problem was what form this anti-tank measure would take. Existing weapons such as hand-emplaced anti-tank grenades could be effective, but the user had to get suicidally close to a target to be sure of getting results, while stand-off rifle grenade warheads were far too small to have much armour penetration. The *Panzerschreck* series was too bulky for general issue. Something novel was obviously required, so the Army Weapon Office (*Hereeswaffenampt*—HWA) issued an urgent requirement for a solution in October 1942; a range of at least 40m (131ft) was requested.

One possible solution was devised by a Doctor Langweiler working at HASAG (Hugo Schneider AG) of Leipzig. Using operational analysis culled from actions on the Eastern Front, by November 1942 Doctor Langweiler had devised a hollow-charge warhead launcher system small enough to be carried and operated by individual soldiers. By March 1943 the first examples were ready for initial trials, where they demonstrated considerable promise.

The new weapon, initially called the *Faustpatrone* (literally Fist Cartridge) or *Faustpatrone* 43, was completely unlike anything seen before. It utilised simplified recoilless gun techniques. A short length of steel tube held the black powder propellant charge, while a 100mm (3.9in) diameter bomb weighing 2.5kg (5.5lb) carrying a

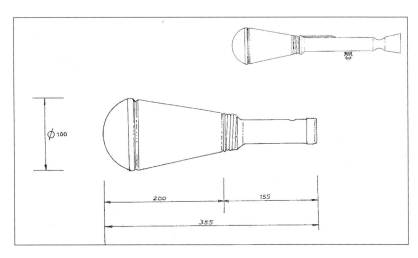

hollow-charge warhead was secured into the tube at one end. The other end of the tube had to be respected for it directed the launch exhaust to the rear. Ignition for the bomb was accomplished using a standard *Eierhandgranate* 39 hand grenade pull igniter.

Early models were intended to be fired by holding the tube horizontally at arms' length and pulling the igniter when ready, but the required stance made accurate aiming difficult. By lengthening the launch tube it became possible to hold the device under an arm or over a shoulder, making aiming much easier and more certain once rudimentary sights were introduced. Troop trials involving a batch of 3,000 pre-production examples of the long tube proposal followed from July 1943 onwards and were considered a great success.

The new weapon with the lengthened launch tube was ordered into production as the *Panzerfaust klein*, nicknamed 'Gretchen', with a range of 30m (c100ft) and a 100mm (3.9in) diameter hollow charge warhead weighing 680g (1.5lb). While this warhead could penetrate 140mm (5.5in) of armour set at an angle of 30°, it was considered that something better would be needed, leading to the almost simultaneous development of a larger 150mm (5.9in) diameter hollow-charge bomb weighing 3kg (6.6lb), containing 1.5kg (3.3lb) of RDX/TNT 60/40. The enlarged warhead model, originally known as the *Panzerfaust gross*, was later renamed the *Panzerfaust* 30M (*Panzerfaust—Armoured Fist*). Penetration was increased to 200mm (7.8in) against armour plate set at an angle of 30°.

Mass production was ordered for both the *Panzerfaust klein* and *Panzerfaust* 30M, initial production rates calling for quantities of 100,000 a month and 200,000 a month respectively. Allied air raids and other production difficulties prevented such targets being achieved before April 1944 but thereafter the planned totals were met or even exceeded. The *Panzerfaust*

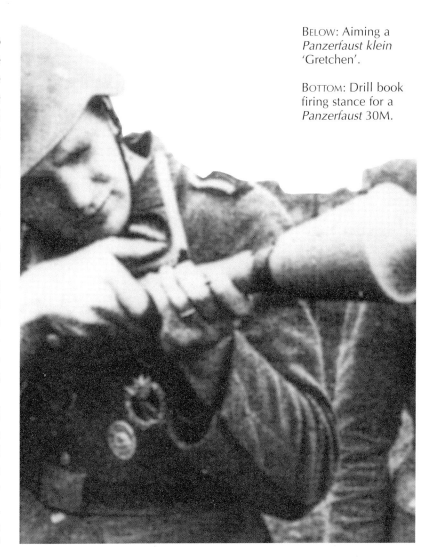

BELOW: Aiming a *Panzerfaust klein* 'Gretchen'.

BOTTOM: Drill book firing stance for a *Panzerfaust* 30M.

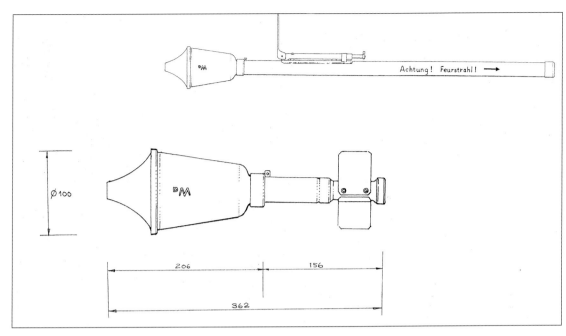

LEFT: Outline drawing of a *Panzerfaust klein*. L. Haywood

BELOW: Comparison drawings of the two main sub types of the *Panzerfaust 30M*. L. Haywood

FAR LEFT: US GIs demonstrate the launching methods for a *Panzerfaust 30M* (front) and a *Panzerwurfmine* (L). While the 30M stance is roughly correct, that for the *Panzerwurfmine* is wrong: the grenade should be swung by the folded tail fins.

klein and *Panzerfaust* 30M both used the same seamless steel launch tube supplied by Volkswagen from its Fallersleben plant. Final production was carried out by R. Tummler at Döbeln in Saxony.

Operation was the same for both models and was closely followed by the later *Panzerfaust* variants. After the bomb had been primed and replaced in its launch tube before issue, each *Panzerfaust* was handed out as a complete item of ammunition with no further preparation required prior to use. Carrying might involve an improvised shoulder sling but that was often lacking. When the time came to launch the *Panzerfaust,* all that was necessary was for the user to tuck the launch tube under the arm or over the shoulder, remove a bomb securing pin and flip up the rear sight to reveal the trigger lever. Aiming was confined to looking through the rear sight and aligning it with a small spike on the bomb body. Pressing the trigger lever cocked and released a spring loaded striker onto a percussion igniter to detonate the black powder charge and propel the bomb from the tube.

As the propellant charge ignited, a tail cap blew off to allow a 2m (6ft 6in) long stream of flame and blast to issue from the rear of the tube; the mass of this efflux was necessary to counterbalance the recoil

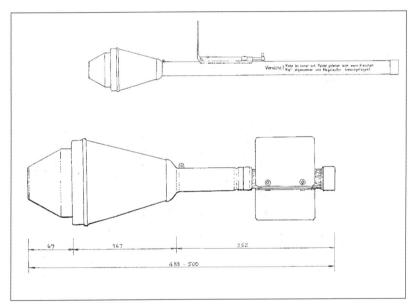

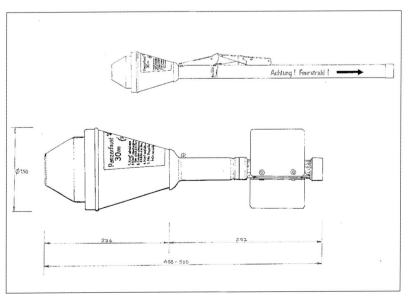

TOP: *Panzerfaust* 30M in a ready to launch condition.

ABOVE: *Panzerfaust* 30M with bomb removed from the launch tube.

forces produced as the bomb was launched. This launch exhaust could be highly dangerous to an unwary user or anyone else in the vicinity, and imposed restrictions as to how and from where the *Panzerfaust* could be deployed. They could not be fired safely from within confined areas, while even in the open a safety area extending 10m (33ft) to the rear was meant to be observed. Warnings against this hazard, and operating instructions generally, were printed on the bomb body so that, in theory, the *Panzerfaust* could be picked up on a battlefield and utilised by an untrained individual.

Despite the simplicity of the *Panzerfaust* concept, training versions were developed and utilised for the *Panzerfaust klein*, 30M and 60M. All involved a reloadable bomb with an inert warhead propelled by two blank 7.92mm rifle cartridges inside a housing extending almost the entire internal length of the launch tube. The rear of this internal tube carried a padded counterweight, propelled to the rear as the bomb was launched to provide an indication of the rearwards hazard area on firing. (See illustration of training versions on page 46.)

Once the bomb had left the launch tube, four rectangular or triangular spring steel fins sprang out from the tail to stabilise the bomb throughout its short and rather slow trajectory arc (the initial velocity was 30m/sec—c100ft/sec). The impact fuze became armed after the bomb had travelled about 3m (10ft). Once the bomb had been fired the launch tube was discarded, making the *Panzerfaust* the first of the one-shot, fire-and-forget, disposable weapons now commonplace.

On impact the *Panzerfaust* 30M's armour penetration capability of 200mm (7.8in) meant that any Allied tank was vulnerable, although stand-off wire mesh or metal plate screens were just as effective a defence against *Panzerfaust* bombs as they were against *Panzerschreck* and Bazooka rockets. Another combat consideration was that the maximum range of only 30m (100ft) demanded considerable motivation and nerve to ensure a hit against an advancing tank.

By the summer of 1944 the *Panzerfaust klein* was being phased out of production in favour of the *Panzerfaust* 60M; the *Panzerfaust* 30M remained in production until early 1945. On the *Panzerfaust* 60M the range was increased to 60m (200ft) by increasing the propellant charge to provide an initial bomb velocity of 45m/sec (c150ft/sec). The bomb remained the same as that for the *Panzerfaust* 30M but the steel launch tube wall thickness had to be increased by 3mm (1/10th of an inch) to withstand the increased charge. To maintain production totals during the change over period a number of *Panzerfaust* 30M bombs were loaded into *Panzerfaust* 60M launch tubes.

Soon after its inception in September 1944 the *Panzerfaust* 100M entered production, the first examples reaching the troops during November. Once again the bomb remained unchanged but range was further increased to 100m (328ft) by the introduction of a two-part propellant charge system resulting in a higher initial

Left: Drill book illustration of a *Panzerfaust* 60M ready to launch.

Below: A typical 1945 photograph of a German defender awaiting the approach of Allied armour while armed only with a *Panzerfaust* 60M.

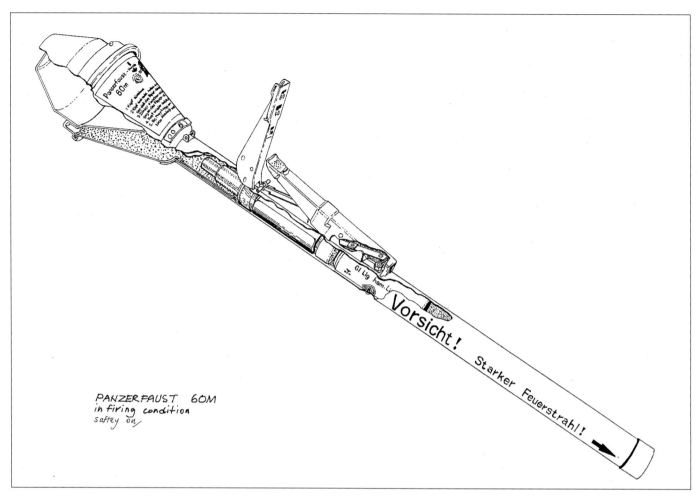

PANZERFAUST 60M
in firing condition
saftey on/

ABOVE: Cross sectioned drawing of a *Panzerfaust* 60M in the firing condition. *L. Haywood*

RIGHT: Illustrations of the instructions printed on a *Panzerfaust* 60M bomb body together with an inset depicting the priming of a *Panzerfaust* 60M bomb. *L. Haywood*

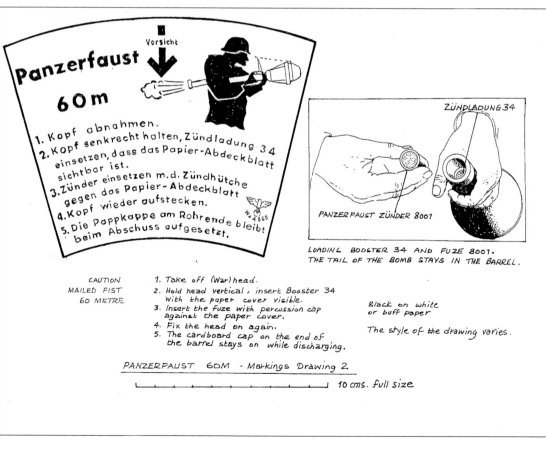

Vorsicht

Panzerfaust
60m

1. Kopf abnehmen.
2. Kopf senkrecht halten, Zündladung 34 einsetzen, dass das Papier-Abdeckblatt sichtbar ist.
3. Zünder einsetzen m.d. Zündhütche gegen das Papier-Abdeckblatt.
4. Kopf wieder aufstecken.
5. Die Pappkappe am Rohrende bleibt beim Abschuss aufgesetzt.

W.a 1865

ZÜNDLADUNG 34

PANZERFAUST ZÜNDER 8001

LOADING BOOSTER 34 AND FUZE 8001.
THE TAIL OF THE BOMB STAYS IN THE BARREL.

CAUTION
MAILED FIST
60 METRE

1. Take off (War)head.
2. Hold head vertical, insert Booster 34 with the paper cover visible.
3. Insert the fuze with percussion cap against the paper cover.
4. Fix the head on again.
5. The cardboard cap on the end of the barrel stays on while discharging.

Black on white
or buff paper

The style of the drawing varies.

PANZERFAUST 60M - Markings Drawing 2

10 cms. full size

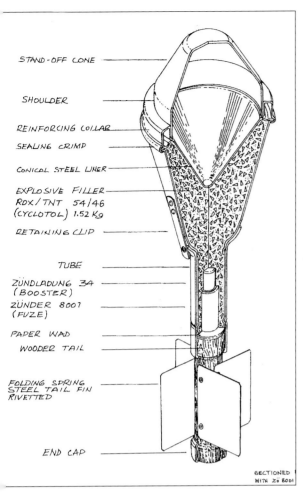

STAND-OFF CONE

SHOULDER

REINFORCING COLLAR

SEALING CRIMP

CONICAL STEEL LINER

EXPLOSIVE FILLER
RDX/TNT 54/46
(CYCLOTOL) 1.52 Kg

RETAINING CLIP

TUBE

ZÜNDLADUNG 34
(BOOSTER)

ZÜNDER 8007
(FUZE)

PAPER WAD

WOODEN TAIL

FOLDING SPRING
STEEL TAIL FIN
RIVETTED

END CAP

SECTIONED
WITH ZÖ 8001

velocity of 62m/sec (c200ft/sec), but ignited in a manageable dual-stage functioning sequence.

In January 1945 yet another model appeared, the *Panzerfaust* 150M, the range increasing yet again to 150m (c500ft). On this model the appearance of the bomb changed. Not only was it improved aerodynamically but the hollow charge carried was smaller, being similar to that used with the *Panzerschreck* rockets, considerably reducing production costs by using less explosive and introducing the economies of scale, while retaining much the same armour penetration as before. The warhead diameter was 105mm (5.9in) .

Not many *Panzerfaust* 150Ms actually reached the troops, even for troop trials. By the time it was ready for production, the manufacturing of all *Panzerfaust* models was becoming increasingly disrupted by Allied air raids and land advances. With the steel production centres of the Ruhr in Allied hands by early 1945, supplies of the mild steel launch tubes became difficult

LEFT: Cross sectioned drawing of a *Panzerfaust* 60M bomb showing the main components. *L. Haywood*

BELOW LEFT: Fully dimensioned drawing of a *Panzerfaust* 60M bomb. *L. Haywood*

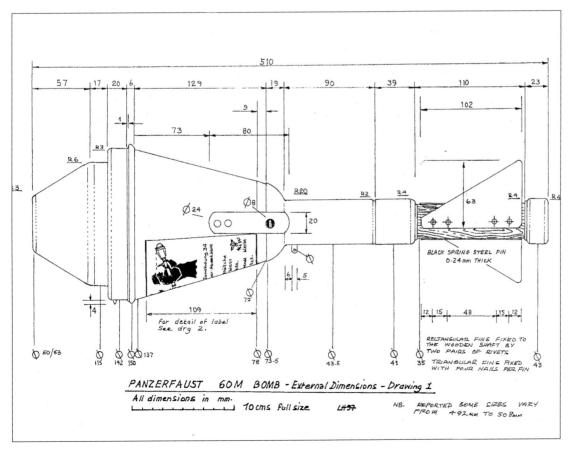

PANZERFAUST 60M BOMB - External Dimensions - Drawing 1

All dimensions in mm.

10cms full size   LH57

NB. REPORTED BOMB SIZES VARY FROM 492mm TO 508mm

RIGHT: Drawings of the *Panzerfaust* 60M and its bomb. Note that the bomb could have tail fins as depicted or others with a triangular outline. *L. Haywood*

BELOW: Drawings of the *Panzerfaust* 100M and its bomb. *L. Haywood*

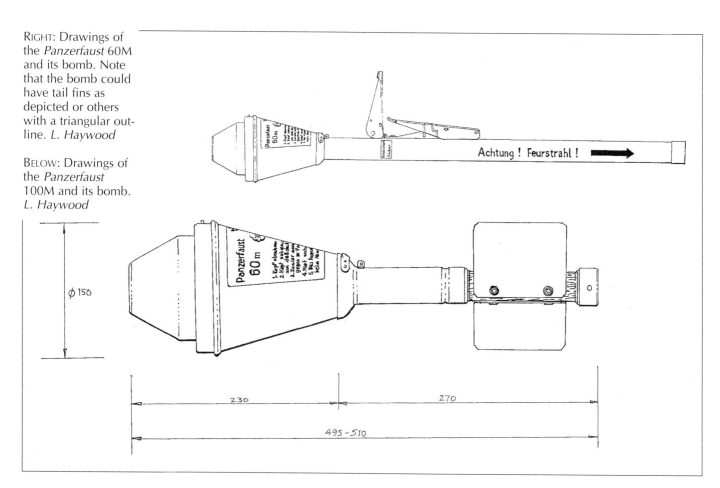

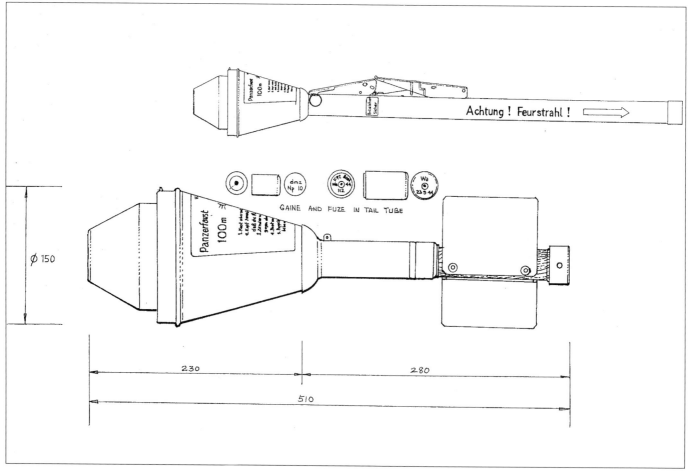

while even black powder supplies dwindled. Yet *Panzerfaust* 60Ms and 100Ms continued to create mayhem among Allied tank formations as *Panzerfausts* were handed out to all and sundry after a minimum of training or preparation. For the hastily raised Hitler Jugend and Volksturm formations, the *Panzerfaust* was just about the only weapon they were given before they were marched off to attempt to somehow stem the Allied advances. There are few late war period German combat photographs that do not show a *Panzerfaust* somewhere in the frame.

By the time the war ended total *Panzerfaust* production had reached 6,700,100, not including the two early models; they alone added a further 1,542,212. Despite these massive industrial efforts the *Panzerfaust* series was still undergoing further enhancements and trials even in the latter days of the war.

HASAG had been responsible for the development of the *Panzerfaust* 150M. As the war ended they were still working on that model's proposed successor, the *Panzerfaust* 250. This greatly improved model was intended to be reloadable using a multi-section propulsion cartridge imparting an initial velocity of up to 150m/sec (500ft/sec) to a revised *Panzerfaust* 150M pattern bomb; maximum range was a planned 250m (820ft). In the event no completed examples were ready before the Allies marched in.

Postwar *Panzerfaust* 250 development under Soviet supervision resulted in the RPG-2, the forerunner of the much-copied and widely issued RPG-7 series, still in widespread production during the late 1990s. In the West the *Panzerfaust* concept is still discernible in many current portable anti-armour weapon systems, especially in the *Panzerfaust* 3 manufactured by Dynamit Nobel of Troisdorf, Germany.

To return to wartime *Panzerfaust* development, the success of the weapon concept for anti-tank use prompted applica-

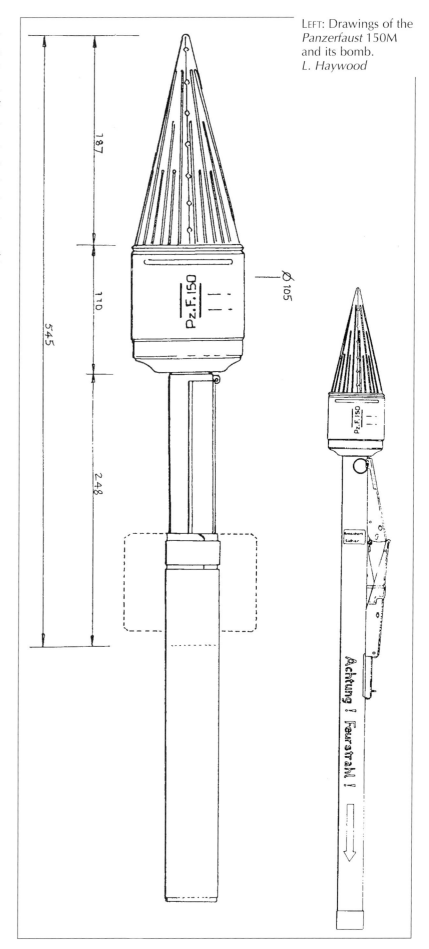

LEFT: Drawings of the *Panzerfaust* 150M and its bomb.
L. Haywood

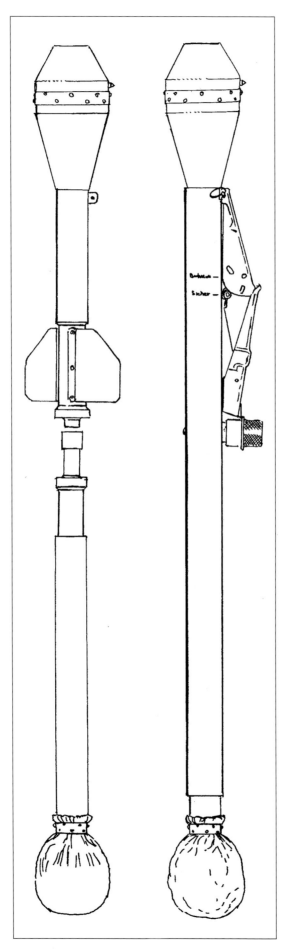

RIGHT: The reloadable training version for the early *Panzerfaust* series with its inert bomb. *L. Haywood*

CENTRE RIGHT: The *Sprengfaust* or *Splitterfaust,* a proposed high explosive/fragmentation version of the *Panzerfaust* which was fully developed but not accepted for service. *L. Haywood*

FAR RIGHT: Drawing of the *Panzerfaust* proposed 250 bomb with propellant attached. *L. Haywood*

tions in other areas. High explosive and incendiary warheads were developed but the latter do not appear to have reached operational status. Neither did a *Sprengranate* 'bouncing bomb' high explosive/fragmentation version, also known as the *Splitterfaust.* This was supposed to spring into the air on impact with the ground to detonate and scatter anti-personnel fragments from its pre-fragmented 88mm (3.4in) diameter warhead over a wide area.

Although development of the *Sprengranate/Splitterfaust* was completed few appear to have been produced as it had been demonstrated that adequate anti-personnel effects could be achieved by simply adding a steel fragmentation collar to standard *Panzerfaust* bombs. As an alternative a self-destruct pellet functioning after two seconds could be added to a standard *Panzerfaust* 60M or 100M bomb fuze, converting the bomb into a potential anti-personnel weapon.

The only other known *Panzerfaust* type weapon of the World War 2 period was produced in Japan late in the war. Little enough is known of it, not even its designation, but it appears to have utilised similar recoilless gun techniques to the *Panzerfaust* and may well have been the end result of a technology transfer from Germany to Japan.

The Japanese *Panzerfaust* utilised a steel tube 890mm (2ft 11in) long having a calibre of 45mm (1.8in). The device launched a bomb weighing 5.3kg (11.7lb) said to be capable of penetrating 120mm (4.7in) of armour; the range of this model was 30-40m (c100-130ft). No sights were involved on the early development models as the tube was aimed from the waist with the base end of the tube, provided with a venturi, placed behind the firer. Five models were apparently intended to be developed, the largest having a range of 100m, but the project appears to have been terminated by the Japanese surrender and few details of any of them now remain.

Panzerfaust

Model	klein 30	30M	60M	100M	150M
Range	30m (c100ft)	30m (c100ft)	60m (c200ft)	100m (c330ft)	150m (c445ft)
Diameter	100mm (3.9in)	150mm (5.9in)	150mm (5.9in)	150mm (5.9in)	105mm (4.1in)
Bomb weight	0.68kg (1.5lb)	3kg (6.6lb)	3kg (6.6lb)	3kg (6.6lb)	3kg (6.6lb)
Total weight	1.5kg (3.3lb)	5.22kg (11.5lb)	6.8kg (15lb)	6.8kg (15lb)	7kg (15.4lb)
Velocity	30m/sec (c100ft/sec)	30m/sec (c100ft/sec)	45m/sec (c150ft/sec)	62m/sec (c200m/sec)	82m/sec (c200m/sec)
Penetration (at 30°)	140mm (5.5in)	200mm (7.8in)	200mm (7.8in)	200mm (7.8in)	200mm (7.8in)

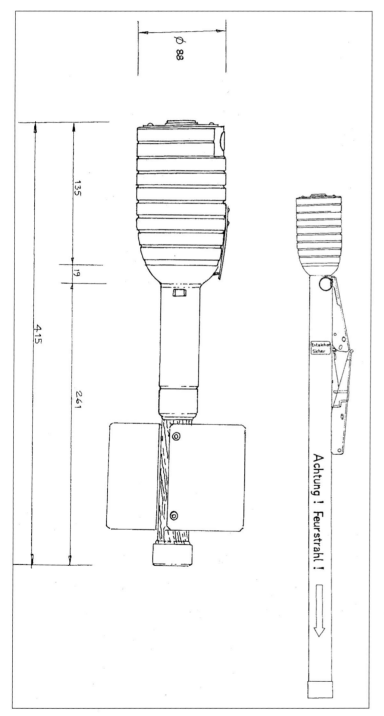

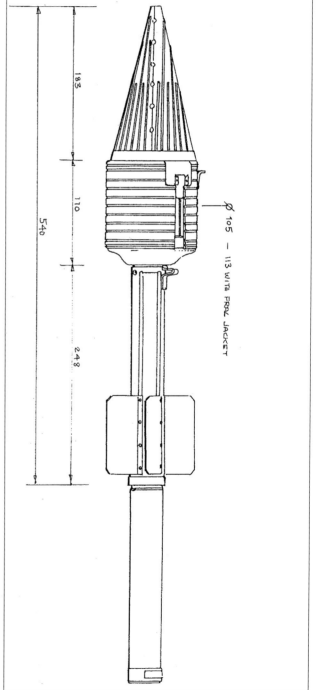

PIAT

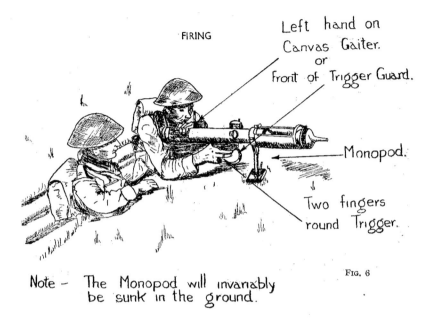

FIRING

Left hand on Canvas Gaiter. or Front of Trigger Guard.

Monopod.

Two fingers round Trigger.

Fig. 6

Note — The Monopod will invariably be sunk in the ground.

ABOVE: The drill book outline of a PIAT ready to fire. [The Drill Book in this case being *Small Arms Training, Projector, Infantry Anti-Tank* as issued by the War Office in 1943.]

RIGHT: The main parts of a PIAT bomb.

THE BRITISH ANTI-TANK equivalent to the *Panzerschreck*, Bazooka and *Panzerfaust* was not a rocket launcher but a form of spigot mortar known as the Projector, Infantry, Anti-Tank, or PIAT. Having said that, the PIAT was deployed in much the same manner as the other weapon systems mentioned above and, as the PIAT projectile carried a hollow charge, it could be equally effective.

Spigot mortars differ from conventional mortars in the way they are loaded and fired. With a conventional mortar a bomb is dropped down a tube for the propellant cartridge to be ignited by contact with a firing pin at the base. With the spigot mortar the hollow tail of the bomb is placed over a tube containing a spring-loaded rod, or spigot, and the propellant cartridge within the bomb tail is ignited by a striker on the end of the spigot after it is released by a trigger mechanism; the tube provides the necessary initial directional guidance for the fired bomb. The spigot mortar scores over the conventional mortar by being able economically to launch projectiles with oversize warheads while remaining relatively light, simple and inexpensive, but it is not so accurate and usually has a shorter range compared to the conventional mortar.

Spigot mortars had their heyday during the Great War of 1914-1918, when it was fashionable to hurl large explosive charges into the trenchworks of the opposing side. During the interwar period and following the introduction of the Stokes Mortar and its progeny, the concept was retained for specialised combat engineer projectors intended to demolish obstacles and strongpoints.

During the interwar years one of the most ardent of the British proponents of the spigot mortar was a Lt-Col Blacker. During

Drum tail

Guide Ring.

Tail Unit.

Body

Fuze Chamber.

the 1930s he was responsible for the development of a spigot mortar based device named the Arbalest which was tested by the British Army in 1939 as a possible infantry support weapon. The contemporary 2in (5.1cm) Mortar was deemed more suitable for infantry use so the Arbalest was rejected at that time.

The post-Dunkirk period of mid-1940 found the British Army lacking in many aspects of modern weaponry, something not assisted by the established peacetime procedures of issuing requirements for new weapons, testing them, passing them fit for service on safety grounds, etc. The associated step-by-step paper-passing necessary to get weapons into the hands of the troops could take months or even years. During 1940 the British could no longer afford such self-imposed luxuries so, despite the opposition of entrenched bureaucracy, some procurement executives devised numerous short cuts to by pass such time consuming processes.

One of these executives involved an ad hoc group of individuals formed within the Directorate of Military Intelligence at the War Office, where a number of serving officers and civilian technicians came together to form a 'think tank' organisation known as MD1. (Later MD1 was transferred for administrative reasons to the Ministry of Supply but remained within the Ministry of Defence orbit.) Within MD1 the normal official procedures were largely overlooked (making them somewhat unpopular in more formal military procurement circles) in attempts to rapidly produce weapons. Their output mainly involved anti-tank weapons, initially for distribution to irregular forces although some of their progeny eventually ended up as general service stores.

From MD1 emanated the 'Sticky Bomb' anti-tank grenades and similar unorthodox weapons, many of which never passed the initial trial stages but which stimulated fresh thought and fresh approaches. From within this organisation Lt-Col Blacker,

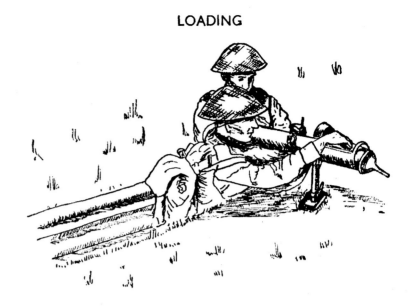

LOADING

Note – The Monopod will invariably be sunk in the ground.

Fig. 5

ABOVE: Loading a PIAT launcher.

who had also become involved with MD1, once again put forward his spigot mortar proposals.

After the Fall of France and the Dunkirk evacuation of June 1940 the British armed forces were in a desperate state as much of their combat equipment had been left in France. Any easily produced weapon that seemed to work was welcomed to somehow fill the many gaps in the armouries so Blacker's Arbalest was modified to become the 29mm (1.1in) Spigot Mortar, more usually known as the Blacker Bombard.

Firing a 6.35 (14lb) or 9.07kg (20lb) high explosive warhead to a range of about 800m (2,600ft) with reasonable accuracy, the Blacker Bombard became a general issue to Home Guard units alongside such hastily derived ordnance exotica as the Northover Projector and the Smith Gun. It was also issued to Royal Air Force units defending airfield perimeters and by some quirk of Army supply some even ended up in North Africa as part of the Tobruk defences. This was probably made possible by the fact that the Blacker Bombard became an approved War Office store in 1941, unlike the Northover and Smith

RIGHT: Right-hand side of a loaded PIAT.

BELOW RIGHT: Left-hand side of a loaded PIAT.

contrivances which were issued only to the Home Guard.

The Blacker Bombard was relatively cheap and easy to produce and could have been quite effective against tanks but it never got much chance to shine. It was essentially a fixed-site weapon as it weighed 156.5kg (364lb) emplaced and the only way to shift it was manually. Blacker therefore decided to produce a more portable counterpart suitable for infantry use which he christened the 'Baby Bombard'. It seemed that his spigot mortar proposals were about to come to full fruition, especially as the British infantry's approved portable anti-tank weapon, the 0.55in (13.97mm) Boys anti-tank rifle, had long since demonstrated itself to be ineffective against the latest German tanks; the British infantry had little else capable of defeating armoured vehicles.

Almost as soon as design work began on his Baby Bombard Lt-Col Blacker was posted away from MD1. His place was taken by a Major Jefferis who went on to develop a portable spigot projector combined with a high explosive bomb. Despite MD1 taking their usual procedural short cuts, the War Office were not impressed with the results and rejected the weapon in August 1941, mainly because the relatively small high explosive warhead bestowed an indifferent anti-armour capability. Major Jefferis was not too discouraged and went on to adapt a hollow charge warhead for the bomb. During early 1942 the Baby Bombard idea, by then renamed as the Jefferis Shoulder Gun, was once again being discussed. By mid-1942 prototypes were being manufactured and tested.

What seems to have turned the tables was not just the hollow charge bomb but

ABOVE: A PIAT crew ready for action, Italy 1944.

LEFT: PIAT ready for action with a spare bomb at hand.

that the spigot mortar concept, carried over to the Jefferis Shoulder Gun, would also allow the firing of high explosive, smoke and other projectiles without modification or loss of range performance, thereby providing the infantry with a versatile support weapon system all of their own extending, it was hoped, to illuminating and target marker bombs. (The latter were destined never to be developed to the in service stage.) Final approval from the War Office was given in late 1942 so that by early 1943 the first examples of the Projector, Infantry, Anti-Tank, or PIAT, were in the hands of the somewhat puzzled British Infantry.

They were puzzled because the PIAT was totally unlike anything they had seen before. 990mm (3ft 3in) long, it resembled a long tubular housing with a padded shoulder piece at one end and a U-shaped trough at the other to accept a bomb weighing 1.35kg (3lb). The tubular steel housing contained a long powerful coil spring carrying the spigot. After cocking, actuating the trigger caused the spring and spigot to fly forward through a bomb locating tube and allow a striker to ignite a cartridge in the tail of the bomb. The resultant detonation projected the bomb from the weapon while the recoil compressed and recocked the spring ready for the manual loading of another bomb ready to fire.

The maximum combat range of the PIAT against tanks was 100m (328ft) although the drum-finned bomb had a maximum possible range of nearly 700m. (c2,300ft). Maximum range against fixed structures, something the instruction manual termed as 'housebreaking', was 320m (1,050ft). The 0.34kg (0.75lb) hollow charge warhead, initiated by a nose fuze, could penetrate at least 100mm (3.9in) of armour. One small item of interest is that when the first PIAT instructors' manual was issued in 1943 the warhead was described as 'high explosive', no doubt in an attempt to conceal its true hollow charge nature for as long as possible.

There was no doubt that the PIAT worked but it was never a popular weapon. One of the most obvious drawbacks for the ordinary foot soldier was the weight of 14.4kg (31.7lb), plus the ammunition, both of which dictated a crew of two; the weight when firing was taken up by a substantial monopod front support. Despite the provision of a sling and sling swivels the PIAT was always an awkward load to carry and handle.

Then there was the problem of cocking the device ready for firing. This involved a feat of strength and expertise. When standing, the operator placed his feet on the extremes of the shoulder piece and pulled

RIGHT: An unusual photograph showing an early PIAT launcher undergoing firing trials while mounted on a modified Crimean war gun carriage.

LEFT: PIAT crew being demonstrated to visiting VIPs and a class of recruits.

BELOW LEFT: The cause of all the trouble—the mainspring of a PIAT being shown to a group of VIPs.

ABOVE: Commando Troop, 1942, with a variety of equipment including: PIAT, Boys Anti-Tank Rifle (behind bicycle's front wheel), scaling ladders, etc.

RIGHT: Airborne troops await an attack: photograph said to be taken during Arnhem September 1944. The PIAT team is in evidence in the immediate foreground (with bayonet fixed); a Bren gunner is further up the road.

upwards using the trigger assembly until the powerful mainspring became cocked. The tubular housing was then lowered until a catch engaged. A bomb could then be loaded. Firing involved the use of two fingers, as the trigger action was long and heavy and resulted in considerable recoil, although it was not unknown for the recoil to be insufficient to recock the mainspring. As far as the firer was concerned the recoil forces were significant but bearable.

Further difficulties arose when the tactical situation did not allow the operator to stand erect while cocking the mainspring. Since the cocking operation required a direct pull of at least 90kg (198lb) the ensuing contortions while the operator struggled from a laying position to overcome the considerable power of the mainspring can

best be left imagined, yet it could be accomplished with practice and proper training. The cocking process could, however, take time and often gave rise to difficulties in combat situations.

Aiming involved a rear sight with two apertures (for an anti-tank range of 65-90m/203-295ft) and a fixed foresight. When the PIAT was fired against structures at ranges of up to 320m (1,050ft) the butt was lowered to the ground with the adjustable front rest fully extended. A small bubble level sight was then employed to obtain the correct angle of elevation.

The PIAT was used by the British Army and its auxiliaries until 1945, some even finding their way into service with European resistance groups, especially in France. It went on to take part in the Korean War, although it was thereafter replaced by the American 3.5in M20 Super Bazooka. Well before 1945 the PIAT had totally supplanted the unloved Boys anti-tank rifle and became the main armament of Universal tracked carriers issued to mechanised infantry units, as well as being mounted on light armoured cars.

PIAT production, mainly by ICI Limited, ran to at least 115,000 units by 1945.

PIAT	
Length overall	990mm (3ft 3in)
Weight	14.4kg (31.7lb)
Velocity	76-137m/sec (250-450ft/sec)
Bomb weight	1.35kg (3lb)
Warhead weight	0.34kg (0.75lb)
Max range	685m (c2,250ft)
Combat range	100m (328ft)
Penetration	100mm (3.9in) plus

Combat and Deployment

ABOVE: A 2.36in M9 launcher in action in Germany during the latter months of the war.

RIGHT: Bocage countryside—dense hedgerows which were perfect for *Panzerschreck* ambush positions and held up the Allied attempt to break out from the Normandy beachhead.

IF THERE WAS any one example of how the power of the then-novel rocket launchers could influence the conduct of military operations it was with the Normandy campaign of June and July 1944. The campaign opened with the 'Overlord' airborne operations and amphibious assault landings along the Normandy beaches on 6 June 1944 and thereafter developed into one of the most prolonged, close quarter slogging matches the Western Allies ever encountered.

Once the landing beaches had been cleared by the British, Canadian and US armies, the intention was to move inland as rapidly as possible along routes cleared by the airborne forces, not only to gain a secure beachhead but to clear space for the forward landing airfields, assembly areas,

supply depots and ammunition dumps that any extension of the Invasion of Europe would demand. About a week after the invasion had commenced some sectors of the beachhead had advanced further than had been anticipated by the forward planners but in others, and especially on the eastern end of the sector along the River Orne and towards Caen, progress was slow and not helped by the determination of the German defenders along the commanding heights they held.

Along other sectors it was the nature of the terrain that was to limit progress during the coming weeks. To the casual traveller the interior of Normandy offers numerous sylvan settings of rural serenity with small farms, orchards and isolated communities seemingly untouched by progress. But to

the military mind the prospect of combat in such areas inspires an entirely different response.

By 1944 the Allied forces had managed by hard experience, thorough training and sheer effort to remould themselves from their infantry-based combat structures of 1940 into more mobile mechanised combat teams capable of inter-service operations in combination with both naval and air forces. It was naval gunfire that provided the heavy artillery support that accompanied the initial landings and during the early stages of the advances into the interior. Once out of range of the naval guns the Allied land forces then had to rely on their own artillery and mortar resources but such resources require forward observers capable of observing relatively wide panoramas to enable the guns under their control to operate to their full effect. Forward observers could also call upon the 'cab rank' squadrons of strike fighters that patrolled the skies above Normandy with minimal interference from a subdued Luftwaffe.

The intention was to utilise these combined resources to allow Allied armour to force a wide route through to the expanses of the Northern French plains and conduct a fluid campaign of tank-based warfare to clear the way to Paris and the rest of France. The emerging problem was that the Allies encountered two of the Germans Army's best defensive assets, the *Panzerschreck* and the Normandy Bocage.

The Bocage is a general name applied to the parts of Normandy made up from small fields, intersecting track networks and small farms that combine to form what emerged as a formidable obstacle to any military movement. The field and orchard systems were networked with ancient boundary hedges and ditches that were quickly recognised as almost perfect defensive barriers. Behind them infantry could remain concealed in ambush ready to open fire against unwary opponents while those same hedges and ditches also provided covered ways for small forces of defenders to switch their positions unobserved when occasion demanded. The small farms and villages could be readily converted to strongpoints on which to anchor defence lines.

Under normal circumstances, isolated pockets of resistance could have been neutralised by combinations of artillery and

ABOVE: Soldiers of the 501st Parachute Regiment moving from Bastogne towards Margeret in December 1944. The leading troops are carrying M9 launchers. Note the method of carrying extra rockets by the soldier on the extreme right.

tank fire or air attack, but within the Bocage the fields of view were so restricted that forward observers and tanks crews could rarely see more than a few metres in front of them, seldom more than the next hedge or line of apple trees. Bringing down artillery and mortar fire or air attack at such ranges was likely to be as dangerous to the Allies as to their opponents, so the brunt of the clearing operations fell to the infantry.

The Bocage fighting could not be conducted by the infantry alone. Although they had to carry out the long and slow close quarter winkling out of their German opposites they had to rely on some form of fire support other than their own portable weapons. In the close confines of their battlefield that had to be provided by tanks. Yet to ensure the tanks could get close enough to their targets the infantry had to escort them every step of the way and somehow eliminate what gradually emerged as the tank's most formidable opponent, the *Panzerschreck*, leading to Allied tank crews having to rely on infantry to clear a path through terrain where *Panzerschrecken* might lurk in ambush. As tanks were originally meant to beat a path for infantry, the *Panzerschreck* managed to impose a complete turn round of armoured and infantry cooperation.

The Bocage formed a perfect combat theatre for the *Panzerschreck*. Combat ranges were short, cover was extensive and along many sectors of the forward lines the battlefield was what came to be known as target rich. The Germans were also determined, disciplined and well-trained defenders. They were well provided with anti-tank guns, especially the infamous 88s which dominated the more open terrain to the east of the bridgehead [see *Classic Weapons: The 88*], and they had the *Panzerschreck*.

They also had tanks, including Panzer VI Tiger Is and Panzer V Panthers, but their impact on the Bocage fighting was limited by the nature of the country as much as for the Allies. The Panzers were just as vulner-

able to Bazookas and PIATs as the Allied tanks were to the *Panzerschreck*. Around the Caen area Panzer units could and did form powerful defensive forces but away to the west towards the country beyond Bayeux, the day-to-day fighting was conducted by the infantry. It was a grim time for the Allied infantry as well as for the German defenders. For days at a time the ranges between attackers and defenders was measured in tens of metres.

Attempting to move forward was always hazardous, especially if tanks were called upon to assist. The bulk of the Allied tanks were M4 Shermans armed with 75mm guns, bulky beasts with relatively thin armour. Their guns could be invaluable in reducing strongpoints yet they, in their turn, were vulnerable to *Panzerschreck* rockets and anti-tank guns so it was the infantry who had to cover their flanks and keep the defenders heads down. Any exposure of a tank to an enemy defensive point almost inevitably resulted in *Panzerschreck* rockets being launched to the detriment of the tank crews. Manoeuvre was difficult as the thick Bocage hedges confined the tanks to the narrow tracks and roads and any attempt to

ABOVE: US infantry squad of 411th Infantry Regiment, 103rd Division, in the Vosges area of France. Note bazooka operator is armed with a Thompson SMG and the covering Browning Automatic Rifle in the centre.

LEFT: 'A dramatic picture from Normandy.' Whether real or just for the camera, it does show the most likely attack quadrant for a bazooka—ie not head-on (see page 61!).

drive over or through the hedges exposed the tanks' thin belly armour to yet more *Panzerschreck* retaliation.

Tank crews attempted all manner of defensive ploys somehow to move forward and gain some form of momentum. Spare tank tracks were slung around tank hulls and turrets along with layers of sandbags to act as stand off protection against the *Panzerschreck* rocket hollow charges but these measures were often no more than a palliative. Tank hulls also sprouted Cullen Prongs on their front hulls, forms of ploughshare devised within the beachhead and intended to cut their way through the thick Bocage hedges.

By the end of July 1944 the fighting in the Bocage had still reached no definite conclusion. The word stalemate was heard more and more, especially as British and Canadian attempts to bypass the Caen area during the massive set piece 'Goodwood' and 'Epsom' battles had been ground to a halt by German anti-tank guns and the few remaining Panzer units still capable of operations, including divisions from two of

the formidable SS Panzer Corps. The Panzers were rendered almost motionless by Allied strike fighters, who swooped on any movements they could detect, yet the area around Caen made the Panzers equally effective as defenders able to act as well-armed mobile bunkers.

Allied morale suffered badly in the aftermath of the 'Goodwood' and 'Epsom' battles while the hard-pressed Allied infantry deployed in the Bocage were making no headway under conditions of summer heat amid farms littered with decaying animal carcasses. Towards the end of July, Allied strengths were already feeling the effects of the prolonged combat with whole divisions being broken up to act as reinforcements to replace front line losses. The bulk of the Allied soldiers, most of them citizen soldiers, were experiencing combat for the first time while many of their German opponents had combat experience from the Eastern Front, if not before.

Yet the German forces were suffering just as much as the Allies and they suffered from weaker numbers. As June and July

LEFT: Target practice in the snow of winter 1944/45 as US infantry replacements fire at knocked-out Panzer IVs. The Ardennes Campaign—Operation '*Wacht am Rhein*'—would give them a chance to put their training into practice.

BELOW: Staged for the cameras (probably with the same tank as that on page 58): an infantry team advances after the Panther has been knocked out. There's 'one up the spout' (fins visible at rear of launcher) but the loader doesn't look too concerned!

BELOW: An unusual combination of two 2.36in M1A1 launchers on a Browning machine gun pintle mounted on an armoured Jeep.

progressed the supplies of fresh personnel and supplies over the Normandy beaches gradually made the Allies stronger as the Germans weakened, until the point was reached in late July when the Allies finally broke through.

The desperate fighting around Caen had concentrated most of the available German reserves to that area. As the Germans concentrated to the east of the beachhead the American divisions to the west were finally able to mass their armoured forces towards Avranches for the Operation 'Cobra' breakthrough which commenced on 25 July with the assistance

of massed bomber formations laying down carpets of bombs to flatten everything in their path. Despite many of the bombs falling on Allied positions, the combined attacks worked and the Americans were through and ready to face east and pass behind and isolate the main German forces. Following an abortive counter attack shattered by air strikes, the Germans withdrew all along the line, heading for the soon to be notorious Falaise Gap despite orders to the contrary from a Hitler still distracted by the 20 July attempt on his life. By the end of the second week of August 1944 the battle for Normandy was effectively over.

Those two desperate months of June and July 1944 were marked not just by the intensity of the fighting but by its close quarter nature imposed by the close confines of the Bocage. Under such conditions all movements, especially the mobile mechanised manoeuvres so favoured by modern tacticians, became impossible as they were countered by weapons such as the *Panzerschreck* which could appear almost anywhere, neutralise any tank operations and then vanish only to reappear somewhere else when least expected. It was a salutary lesson to all military planners of the power and capabilities of what was after all a simple and relatively low cost weapon.

The impact of the Normandy fighting has not been forgotten. Over 50 years later the campaign still serves as an object lesson in the form of combat that any future armed force could experience, for despite the adoption of inter-arm and inter-service tactics and operational methods, matters can still go seriously wrong when shoulder-launched hollow charge weapons appear among terrain closely suited to their capabilities. The long-range guided missile might be the most effective anti-tank weapon of today yet the *Panzerschreck* and Bazooka that did so much to upset the old attack/defence balance still cast their shadows.

LEFT: Another attack for the cameras—infantrymen in Normandy; note rifle grenade launcher in foreground and bazooka team with launcher and projectiles.

BELOW LEFT: In earnest—US Army soldiers turning a captured 8.8cm RP 54 against its former owners, Germany, 1945.

RIGHT: Title page from a set of training cards denoting the type of target and point of aim for a RPzB 54 against Allied tanks

BELOW RIGHT: An 8.8cm RPzB 54 at the instant of launching a rocket—note the self-protective position of the loader in the background.

Panzerbeſchüß-Tafel

Nr. 25

8,8 cm R Pz B 54

(Panzerschreck)

mit

8,8 cm R Pz B Gr 4322

Wirkung

■ = Vernichtende Wirkung

▨ = Behindernde, teilweise vernichtende Wirkung

□ = Keine Wirkung

Angaben über die Waffe und ihre Bedienung, über Haltepunkte, Vorhaltemaße usw. bringt die **D 1864/1**

Nicht in Feindeshand fallen lassen!

Entfernung 12
bis 150 m

Stand: 6.44

Gen St d H / Der Panzeroffizier
Wa Prüf 1/W

	Front	Seite	Heck
T 34			
KW			
Mk II (Matilda)			
Mk IV (Churchill)			
M 4 (Sherman)